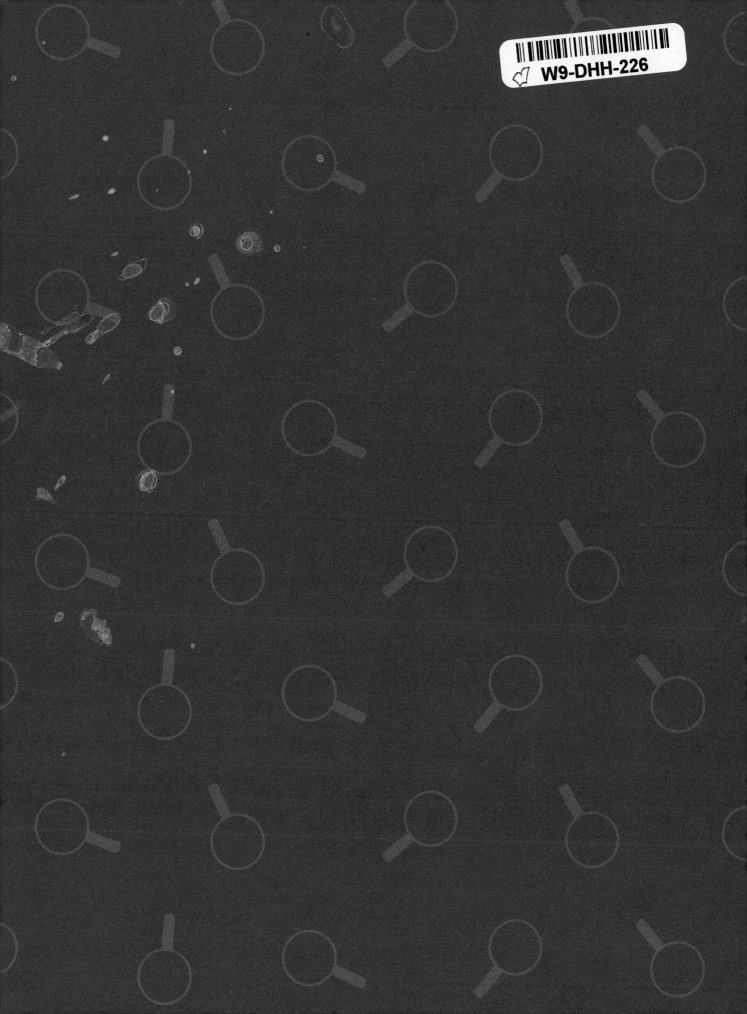

Mystery Solvers

SAFARI SECRET

Bath New York Singapore Hong Kong Cologne Delhi Melbourne

Written by Moira Butterfield
Illustrated by Martha Hardy, Jan Smith
and Jane Swift.

First published by Parragon in 2007

Parragon
Queen Street House
4 Queen Street
Bath BA1 1HE, UK

ISBN 978-1-4054-9543-1

Printed in China
Please retain this information for future reference.

MYSTERY SOLVER
MAGNIFY THE MYSTERY!

Hi there! My name is Detective Dog.

I collect mysteries, passed on to me by other dogs.

Dogs see, smell, and dig better than anyone. They make great detectives.

These mysteries can only be solved by looking at tiny details and finding mini secrets – the kind of thing a dog does brilliantly.

You can do it, too, by using your brains and your magnifying glass.

Good luck. **Woof!**

This story was told to me by my dog friend, Monty. Strange things once happened to him and his owners, twins Sally and Ben.

THE ANSWERS ARE AT THE BACK, BUT GOOD DETECTIVES DON'T LOOK UNTIL THE END.

TOP TWINS TV!

Twins Sally and Ben decided to enter a television competition called **TOP TWINS!**

EIGHT TEAMS OF TWINS COMPETED IN CHALLENGES AROUND THE WORLD TO SEE WHO WAS THE SMARTEST. SALLY AND BEN WERE ALLOWED TO TAKE ALONG THEIR DOG, MONTY.

SALLY   MONTY   BEN

THE COMPETITION BEGAN AT A CITY ZOO.

Welcome to **TOP TWINS!** My name is Freda.

And I'm Joe. Freda and I will be your presenters for the competition this year.

AT EACH LOCATION, THE TEAMS WERE GIVEN CHALLENGES. THE FIRST ONE STARTED AT THE ZOO.

SCORE FOR YOURSELF
Each team has been given a camera. They have all kinds of things to find in each challenge to win points for the competition. You can play, too, by using a pen and paper to keep score as you find things with your magnifying glass.

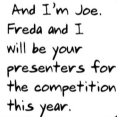

SABOTAGE!
Someone isn't playing fair! Use your magnifying glass to read about three things someone has stolen to sabotage the competition.

1. A camera stolen from one of the teams. 2. A pair of glasses stolen from one of the teams. 3. A shoe stolen from a team member. Can you find them all in the picture?

THE ZOO CHALLENGE

Here is the first test. Find and take photos of these pairs around the zoo. Score two points for each pair that you find.

Two parrots with blue tails.

Two pails with red handles.

Two lizards with purple tail tips.

Two rabbits with white patches.

5

AMAZING AMAZON!

For the next episode, the television crew flew the twin teams to a specially selected section of the Amazon jungle.

Welcome to the jungle. There are a lot of unusual animals here, such as this poisonous snake.

Oh no! It's not there anymore! But I thought the cage was locked!

Watch out, Ben! The snake is under your chair!

Woof, woof!

THE SNAKE WAS SAFELY CAUGHT AGAIN, BUT ITS ESCAPE FROM A SEEMINGLY LOCKED CAGE WAS A MYSTERY. BEFORE SALLY AND BEN COULD QUESTION IT FURTHER, THE TWINS WERE HANDED THEIR NEXT TEST.

THE JUNGLE CHALLENGE

Here is your next test. Find and take photos of these pairs around the jungle. Score two points for each pair that you find.

Two hummingbirds with green wings and red beaks.

Two monkeys with black tail tips.

Two black-and-yellow tree frogs.

Two blue butterflies.

SABOTAGE!
The mystery cheat has been trying to sabotage the competition again. Use your magnifying glass to discover what tricks they've been up to this time.

Can you find five spiders planted in the jungle to score the teams?

7

AFRICAN ADVENTURE!

The next leg of the competition was in the Serengeti, a vast grassland in Africa.

SALLY AND BEN HAD AN EARLY SETBACK WHEN THEY FOUND THAT A TIRE ON THEIR JEEP WAS FLAT.

Luckily, I know how to change it before we can start.

I think the tire has been deflated deliberately.

BUT TWO OTHER TEAMS WEREN'T SO LUCKY.

Good evening, viewers. Two teams have had to pull out of the competition, through regrettable accidents and equipment failure.

I'm beginning to think someone might be out to ruin this competition.

Hmm, then let's show them just how smart we are!

THE AFRICA CHALLENGE

Here is your next TOP TWINS test. Find and take photos of these pairs around the grassland. Score two points for each pair that you find.

Two identical zebras.

Two yellow lizards.

Two giraffes with the same patterned skin.

Two lions with black tail tips.

SABOTAGE!

Someone has been stealing from other contestants and throwing things out of the jeep. Use your magnifying glass to find out which items have been stolen.

1. A water bottle. 2. A sun hat. 3. A pair of sunglasses. Can you find them in the picture!

AROUND THE REEF!

The next stop was the Pacific Ocean for an extra-tough underwater challenge.

THIS TIME THE SABOTEUR NEARLY SLIPPED UP THE NIGHT BEFORE THE TELEVISION SHOW. THE TEAMS WERE CAMPING NEAR THE OCEAN.

Monty, what is it?

Woof, woof!

It's just a seagull. Let's get some sleep.

BUT NEXT MORNING, AT THE START OF THE SHOW…

Another team has had to pull out of the competition as their diving equipment was stolen last night.

It's true, then. Somebody is definitely out to cheat!

THE UNDERWATER CHALLENGE

Here is your next TOP TWINS test. Find and take photos of these pairs underwater. Score two points for each pair that you find.

Two red-and-black fish with three stripes.

Two oysters with a black pearl inside.

Two blue-and-pink fish with the same spots.

Two matching red shells.

SABOTAGE!
The mystery saboteur has thrown diving equipment into the sea. Use your magnifying glass to find out which three pieces of equipment are in the sea.

1. Two flippers 2. A diving mask 3. A diving belt. Can you find them?

FOREST FORTUNES!

Now there were only five teams left in the competition.

This contest is proving more difficult than we thought, folks. Who will make it through the forest challenge?

We've had another disaster. We've lost everyone's scores! They were on a computer disc and it's gone!

Hold on. What's Monty searching for?

You found it, Monty! Well done!

Phew! Well done to that dog! We can go on with the competition.

THE FOREST CHALLENGE

Here is your next TOP TWINS test. Find and take photos of these pairs in the forest. Score two points for each pair that you find.

Two bats hanging upside down.

Two foxes with black-tipped tails.

Two matching toadstools.

Two matching mice.

SABOTAGE!
The mystery cheat has tried to fool the teams by planting fake animals in the forest. Use your magnifying glass to find the fake animals in the scene.

Can you find four fake animals with wind-up mechanical keys?

13

THE MEADOW CHALLENGE

Two matching flowers.

Two lambs with one black and one white ear.

Two matching frogs.

Two matching bird's eggs.

SABOTAGE!
This time, the mystery saboteur has stolen three things from the film crew. Use your magnifying glass to find out which items have been stolen.

1. A cell phone. 2. A wallet. 3. A bunch of keys. Can you find them in the picture?

15

THE PARK CHALLENGE

Here is your next TOP TWINS test. Find and take photos of these pairs in the city park. Score two points for each pair that you find.

Two matching city cats.

Two parrots who have escaped from the zoo.

Two matching puppy dogs.

Two matching rats.

SABOTAGE!

At the end of the broadcast, the teams find that all of the park gates are locked! Use your magnifying glass to find out what the teams need to help them escape.

Can you find five gate keys hidden around the park?

17

DESERT DISASTER!

Ben and Sally decided to try to keep a lookout on the next location: a Mexican desert.

THE NIGHT BEFORE THE SHOW WAS TO BE FILMED, EVERYONE WAS CAMPING IN THE DESERT.

Have you seen anything?

No. Let's get some rest.

THE NEXT MORNING NOTHING SEEMED TO BE WRONG, AT FIRST.

Hi folks. Today we have four teams left in our challenge. Oh, er, actually make that three teams.

What's happened to the missing team?

They're asleep. I think they've been given a sleeping potion.

Here is your next TOP TWINS test. Find and take photos of these pairs in the desert. Score two points for each pair that you find.

Two lizards with matching markings.

Two red desert scorpions.

Two cacti with red flowers.

Two elf owls.

SABOTAGE!

The mystery cheat has been trying to sabotage the competition again. Use your magnifying glass to discover what tricks they've been up to this time.

Can you find four poisonous rattlesnakes planted in the desert to scare the teams?

ARCTIC AWAY DAY!

By now the remaining three teams all suspected each other of being the cheats.

I think it's that team with the dog.

It could be either of the other teams.

JUST AS FILMING WAS ABOUT TO START THERE WAS MORE BAD NEWS.

Oh, no! One of the teams has had their skidoo sabotaged. This will delay the show again.

Hmm. I don't think the cheat is in another team. I think it's someone working on the show.

SALLY TOLD THE REMAINING TEAMS OF HER SUSPICIONS.

Ok, let's work together. We'll beat the cheat!

THE ARCTIC CHALLENGE

Here is your next TOP TWINS test. Find and take photos of these pairs in the Arctic. Score two points for each pair that you find.

Two lemmings with the same markings (lemmings look like little hamsters).

Two reindeer with matching antlers.

Two clusters of red Arctic poppies.

Two birds with matching wings.

SABOTAGE!
The cheat has sabotaged one of the skidoos. Some of its parts are in this picture. Use your magnifying glass to find out which parts are in the Arctic scene.

1. A screw 2. A wing mirror 3. A set of keys 4. An oil can. Can you find them in the picture?

ANTARCTIC ACTION!

The next show came from the other side of the world, in the Antarctic. By now, TOP TWINS was getting a big audience.

MEANWHILE SALLY AND BEN HAD DONE SOME RESEARCH ON THE TELEVISION PRESENTERS.

Joe got fired for knocking over the chessboard during a world championship chess match.

Freda was fired for accidentally setting a studio on fire during a cooking show.

So they could both do with some more success, and they're both benefiting from the big ratings we're getting to watch our disasters.

Either one could be a cheat!

Fingers crossed nothing else goes wrong. Let the show begin!

Here is your next TOP TWINS test. Find and take photos of these pairs in the Antarctic. Score two points for each pair that you find.

Two penguins with a green ring on one leg.

Two penguins with a red ring on one leg.

Two penguins with a purple ring on one leg.

Two birds with a yellow ring on one leg.

SABOTAGE!
This time the mystery saboteur has stolen the same two items from each of the three remaining teams. Use your magnifying glass to find out which items have been stolen.

Can you see three pens and notebooks in the scene?

TIDAL POOL RESCUE!

The next television show came from the beach, where the remaining teams were given directions to a group of tidal pools.

THE SHOW WAS HALFWAY THROUGH, AND THE TEAMS WERE BUSY SEARCHING FOR ANIMALS WHEN SUDDENLY…

Help!

It's Freda! She's sinking in quick sand by that black rock!

THE TEAMS RUSHED TO HELP HER.

Hold on, Freda! We'll pull you out!

Well folks, Freda is OK, but sadly, none of the teams have completed the challenge.

MEANWHILE, SALLY ASKED FREDA WHO HAD TOLD HER TO STAND BY THE BLACK ROCK.

THE TIDAL POOL CHALLENGE

Here is your next TOP TWINS test. Find and take photos of these pairs in the tidal pools. Score two points for each pair that you find.

Two crabs with blue spots.

Two shells with pink stripes.

Two little fish with purple tails.

Two seagulls with red collars on.

SABOTAGE!

At last! The saboteur has left behind a clue. Monty has sniffed it out on the beach. Use your magnifying glass to find out what Monty has found.

Monty has found a rolled-up map of the beach. Can you find it in the scene?

AND THE WINNER IS...

At last the final result was to be announced back at the zoo in front of millions of viewers.

Nobody completed the final challenge, so nobody has won!

That's because you cheated, Joe!

You can't prove that!

Oh yes, we can. We know that you have a twin. It's him, the cameraman!

GOOD OLD MONTY FOUND A PHOTO IN JOE'S POCKET OF HIM AND HIS TWIN. IT TURNED OUT THAT THE BROTHERS HAD ONCE LOST THE COMPETITION AND WERE OUT FOR REVENGE, AS WELL AS TELEVISION SUCCESS. THEY DELIBERATELY WRECKED THE SHOW WHILE GETTING BIG TV AUDIENCES FOR THEMSELVES.

The twins found a way out of the zoo, while avoiding the security cameras. Can you work out which way they went?

You'll never catch us!

ANSWERS

Pages 4–5
- ○ Challenge
- ○ Sabotage

Pages 6–7
- ○ Challenge
- ○ Sabotage

Pages 8–9
- ○ Challenge
- ○ Sabotage

Pages 10–11
○ Challenge
○ Sabotage

Pages 12–13
○ Challenge
○ Sabotage

Pages 14–15
○ Challenge
○ Sabotage

ANSWERS

Pages 16 –17
- ⭘ Challenge
- ⭘ Sabotage

Pages 18–19
- ⭘ Challenge
- ⭘ Sabotage

Pages 20 –21
- ⭘ Challenge
- ⭘ Sabotage

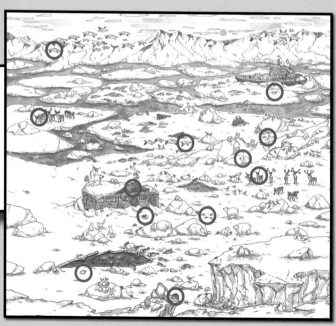

Pages 22–23

○ Challenge

○ Sabotage

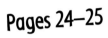

Pages 24–25

○ Challenge

○ Sabotage

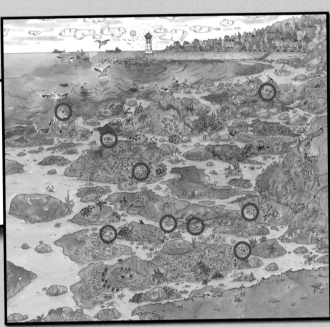

Pages 26–27

○ Challenge

ANSWERS

Pages 26–27

—— Route taken